Material Properties

1. List all the different materials you can see around you.

   _____
   _____
   _____

2. Choose two materials that are different. Why are they different?

   _____
   _____

3. Choose two materials that are similar. Why are they similar?

   _____
   _____

4a Which is the most important property of material for a cycling helmet to have?

   _____

4b Why?

   _____

Identifying Materials

1 Draw a large and a small object made from the different materials in this table.

	Large	Small
Wood		
Metal		
Plastic		
Rubber		

Uses of Materials

Some objects are made from more than one type of material.

2   Draw two objects that are made from both plastic and another material.

3   Label the other materials they are made from.

Object 1

Object 2

Identifying Properties of Materials

1 Record two different ways of putting different materials into two groups using opposite properties. Draw and label the materials in each group.

The opposite properties of these two groups are

_____

The opposite properties of these two groups are

_____

Uses of Materials

2a Choose five pairs of different materials.

2b For each pair, identify which properties are similar. Identify which properties are different.

2c Record your ideas in the table below.

Pair of materials	Similar properties	Different properties

Suitable Materials: Mark Making

There are many different types of things we use to make marks. They are all used for slightly different jobs.

1. Identify the objects used to make marks in the diagrams below.

2. Choose two that are used for slightly different jobs. What is each one used for?

A _____ is used _____

A _____ is used _____

Suitable Materials: Footwear

1 Choose four different types of footwear you use. Draw and label them. Record when you wear them.

I wear _____ when I _____	I wear _____ when I _____
I wear _____ when I _____	I wear _____ when I _____

Thermochromic Materials

These ducks are made from a thermochromic material. This means they change colour really quickly when the temperature changes.

1 Why might it be useful for a rubber duck to change colour when it gets hot?

_____
_____

2 Find out other ways thermochromic materials are used. Choose one. Draw and write about it.

Precious Materials

1 Choose a precious material to find out about.

Make a fact sheet about it. Include where it comes from and what it is used for.

Science Skills

Record it!

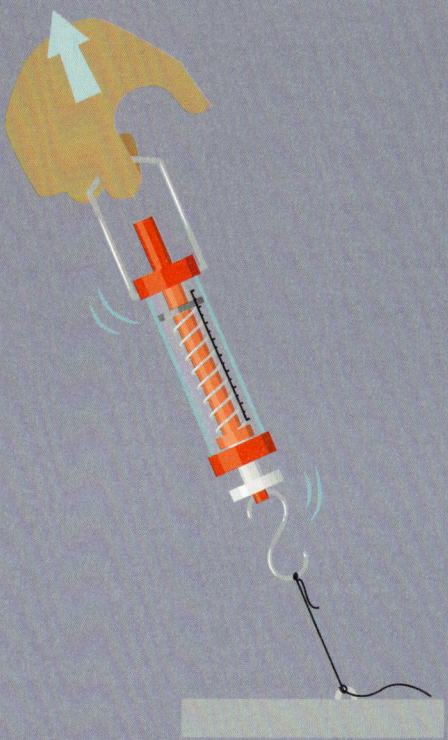

A scientist has been asked to find the breaking strengths of different threads. They found out that cotton needed a force of 2N to break. Wool needed a force of 5N. Silk and twine both had a breaking strength of 8N and string needed a force of 11N.

1   Record these results as a list.

Uses of Materials

2. Draw a picture that shows the results.

3. Show the results in a table.

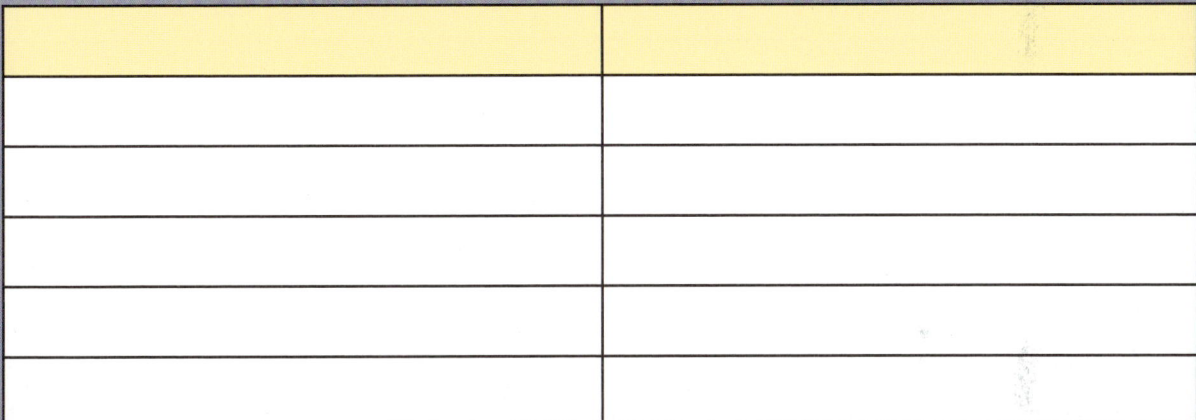

4. Draw the results on a chart.

Absorbent Materials

1a List four absorbent materials.

1b Record when they are used.

Absorbent material	When used

We usually clean up a spill on the floor using a mop.

2 If you do not have a mop what other things could you use to clean up the spill?

Science Skills

Predict it!

Kitchen roll • Cleaning cloth • Washing-up sponge • Paper towel • Metal foil • Plastic carrier-bag

1. Look at the materials drawn above. Predict which will absorb water. Record your ideas below.

2. Order the materials you think are absorbent materials from most to least absorbent.

Most absorbant	Least absorbant

Waterproof Materials

1. Draw four objects that need to be waterproof. Label the objects. Explain why they need to be waterproof.

A _____ needs to be waterproof because _____ _____

A _____ needs to be waterproof because _____ _____

A _____ needs to be waterproof because _____ _____

A _____ needs to be waterproof because _____ _____

Science Skills

Test it!

We can do a test to find out which materials are waterproof.

1. You can only use the equipment in the diagram. Plan how you would do the test. Record your plan in the space below. You can write and draw pictures.

Suitable and Unsuitable Materials

1. List three of the materials used to make a nappy and record why each material is suitable.

   Material 1: _____ is used

   _____

   Material 2: _____ is used

   _____

   Material 3: _____ is used

   _____

2. Why would you *not* use glass to make a nappy?

   _____

3. List two *unsuitable* materials to make a t-shirt. Record why they are unsuitable.

   _____ is unsuitable because _____

   _____

   _____ is unsuitable because _____

   _____